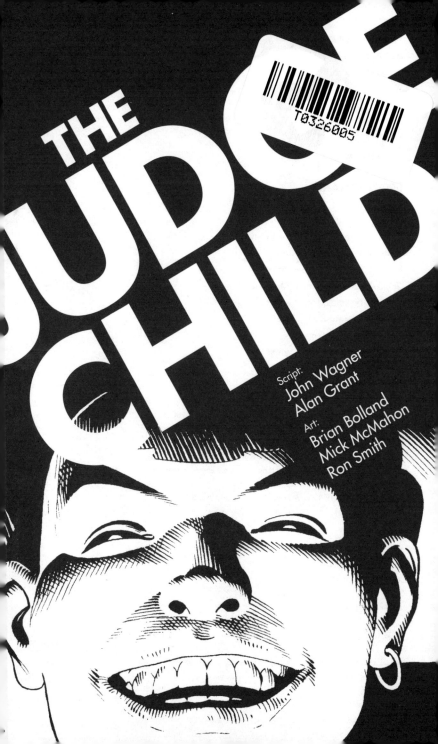

JOHN WAGNER
ALAN GRANT
Writers

BRIAN BOLLAND
MICK MCMAHON
RON SMITH
Artists

BRIAN BOLLAND
Cover Artist

Creative Director and CEO: Jason Kingsley
Chief Technical Officer: Chris Kingsley
Publishing Manager: Ben Smith
2000 AD Editor in Chief: Matt Smith
Graphic Novels Editor: Keith Richardson
Graphic Design: Simon Parr
PR: Michael Molcher
Reprographics: Kathryn Symes
Original Commissioning Editor:
Steve MacManus

Published by Rebellion, Riverside House, Osney Mead, Oxford OX2 0ES
www.rebellion.co.uk

ISBN: 978-1-78108-109-9
Printed by CPI Bookmarque
First published: March 2013
10 9 8 7 6 5 4 3 2 1

Printed on FSC Accredited Paper

A CIP catalogue record for this book is available from the British Library.

For information on other 2000 AD graphic novels, or if you have any comments
on this book, please email books@2000ADonline.com

To find out more about 2000 AD, visit www.2000ADonline.com

IN ORBIT
EVERY
MONDAY

PROG 161

Malaysia $1.00
New Zealand 36c
Australia 36c
South Africa 36c
Mercury 17p
Venus 10p
Mars 18p
Asteroid Belt 20p
Saturn 84p
Neptune 87p
Pluto 5½p

12p
EARTH
MONEY

19 APR 80

SULPHUR SAND — IT'S S-SUCKING ME IN! HELP ME, JUDGE!

THAT ALL DEPENDS ON THE **ANSWERS** YOU GIVE ME...

ANSWERS? ANSWERS TO **WHAT**, DROKK YA?

SIX MONTHS AGO SLAVERS ATTACKED A SETTLEMENT EAST OF HERE. THIS BOY, **OWEN KRYSLER**, WAS TAKEN. I **WANT** THAT BOY!

OUR STORY BEGINS MANY DAYS EARLIER AND FAR TO THE EAST. BENEATH THE HALL OF JUSTICE IN MEGA-CITY ONE IS THE DEPARTMENT KNOWN AS **THE VAULTS** —

DEATH CREEPS UP ON ME AT LAST, CHIEF JUDGE. I ASKED... TO BE KEPT ALIVE UNTIL YOU ARRIVED. I HAVE HAD A VISION... A **TERRIBLE PROPHECY** —

JUDGE FEYY WAS THE CITY'S OLDEST **PRE-COG**. HIS VISIONS OF THE FUTURE WERE 88·8% ACCURATE —

I SAW A **WAR** MORE **GHASTLY** THAN ANY WE HAVE KNOWN. I SAW OUR CITY **DESTROYED** — AND FROM THE DESTRUCTION **FOUL CREATURES** ROSE TO PREY ON THE SURVIVORS...!

THIS WILL HAPPEN IN THE YEAR 2120.

BUT THERE IS ONE WHO CAN **SAVE** US. I HAVE SEEN HIM. A CHILD BORN OF THIS CITY...

HE IS NO ORDINARY BOY. ON HIS HEAD HE BEARS THE **EAGLE OF JUSTICE**... HE IS FATED TO **RULE** MEGA-CITY ONE IN ITS **GRAVEST HOUR**.

I HAVE ONLY A NAME — **OWEN KRYSLER**. HE CAN GUIDE US THROUGH THE DARKNESS. FIND HIM —

FIND THE JUDGE CHILD!

MANY OF OUR PRE-COGS HAVE PREDICTED A TIME OF CRISIS IN THE EARLY 'TWENTIES. THIS IS THE CLEAREST VISION WE'VE HAD OF IT YET.

THERE ARE 47 OWEN KRYSLERS IN THE CITY. NONE OF THEM FITS JUDGE FEYY'S DESCRIPTION.

BUT THERE WAS *ONE OTHER* OWEN KRYSLER. HE LEFT THE CITY FOUR YEARS AGO WITH HIS PARENTS TO SETTLE IN THE NEW MUTIELAND TERRITORIES. THAT'S ALL WE KNOW.

AND YOU WANT ME TO CHECK ON HIM... ?

IT MIGHT BE A WILD GOOSE CHASE — JUDGE FEYY COULD BE *WRONG*. BUT WE CAN'T TAKE THE CHANCE. THE BOY COULD BE THE ONLY HOPE FOR MEGA-CITY ONE !

IT WAS MANY DAYS LATER WHEN JUDGE DREDD FOUND THE SETTLEMENT...

DROKK ! WHAT'S HAPPENED HERE ?

SLAVE*R*S GOT 'EM ! TOOK WHAT THEY WANTED AND STRUNG UP THE REST — ALL 'CEPT ME ! SAID I WAS SO *UGLY*, THE CRUELLEST THING WAS TO LET ME LIVE ! RECKON THEY WAS RIGHT, TOO !

I'M LOOKING FOR PEOPLE CALLED KRYSLER.

YOU COME TO THE RIGHT PLACE, JUDGE. *THAT'S* THE KRYSLERS ! LOVELY COUPLE, AIN'T THEY ?

THE BOY — WHAT HAPPENED TO HIM ?

SLAVERS TOOK HIM !

DREDD FOUND THE HOLOGRAM INSIDE THE HOUSE —

A BIRTHMARK LIKE THE EAGLE OF JUSTICE ! *IT'S HIM !*

8

NOW, A WEEK LATER, DREDD HAD LOCATED THE GROUP OF SLAVERS —

THAT MARK! YEAH, I RECOGNISE THE KID — I REMEMBER HIM GOOD! HE WAS A REAL STRANGE ONE...

THE KID DIDN'T CRY WHEN WE STRUNG UP HIS MA AN' PA! DIDN'T MAKE NO FUSS AT ALL! IT WAS LIKE HE *KNEW* IT WOULD HAPPEN!

I MUST GO ON MY JOURNEY NOW. GOODBYE, MOTHER. GOODBYE, FATHER. WE WILL MEET AGAIN IN ANOTHER PLACE.

AND THE *BOY*?

WE THOUGHT WE'D GET A GOOD PRICE FOR A STRANGE KID LIKE THAT. SOME OF THE GUYS TOOK HIM TO THE *SLAVE MARKET* IN *NEUTRON FLATS*. THAT'S ALL I KNOW!

HE'S ALL YOURS, BOYS!

HEY, WAIT! YOU PROMISED!

I KEPT MY PROMISE. YOU'RE *OUT* OF THE SULPHUR SAND.

YOU'RE GONNA *DANGLE*, SLAVER!

JUST LIKE ALL YOUR INNOCENT VICTIMS!

DREDD REPAIRED HIS BIKE AND SENT OFF A MESSAGE POD —

RADIO CONTACT'S IMPOSSIBLE THROUGH THE CURSED EARTH. THE POD'LL CARRY WORD BACK TO MEGA-CITY ONE.

THE MORE I LEARN OF THIS BOY, THE MORE CERTAIN I BECOME THAT HE *IS THE JUDGE CHILD*. I WON'T REST UNTIL I'VE FOUND HIM!

NEXT PROG: "WHAT AM I BID FOR JUDGE DREDD!?"

9

ALL CLEAR !

UNDRESS THAT CREEP AND DITCH HIM SOMEWHERE !

AS DREDD'S BIKE SPED OFF, THE NEW "BROTHER MONKEYWRENCH" ENTERED THE TEMPLE OF TRASH –

YOUR BURIAL SHROUD IS READY, FARO ! MADE ENTIRELY OF PRICELESS RING-PULL TABS, AS YOU ORDERED !

TEN WAGON-LOADS OF BEST GARBAGE ARE COMING IN FROM THE MINES !

EXCELLENT ! I WILL TAKE MY WORLDLY FORTUNE WITH ME TO THE SPIRIT WORLD !

DREDD HEADED FOR FARO'S NEEDLE –

I'M GOING TO PREPARE THE BOY FOR THE FUNERAL.

PASS, BROTHER BUNSEN !

SO IT'S TIME. YOU'VE BROUGHT THE DRUG...

NO USE HIDING IT FROM YOU, IS THERE, KID ? YOU KNOW EVERYTHING !

NOT EVERYTHING. I SEE THE NEEDLE, BUT THEN... ONLY SHADOWS...

THE SLAVES ARE GETTING RESTLESS, BROTHER BUNSEN! HEY — YOU'RE LEAVING!

TOO RIGHT! IT'S BEEN A GREAT RACKET, BUT WITHOUT FARO ALL HELL'S GONNA BREAK LOOSE! TAKE MY ADVICE — GRAB WHAT YOU CAN AND BEAT IT WHILE THE GETTING'S GOOD!

BETCHA GOT SOME GOOD GARBAGE IN THE BOX, HUH?

BETTER THAN GARBAGE, SON, THE BEST PRIZE OF ALL!

JUDGE DREDD WAS AMONG THOSE CHOSEN FOR SACRIFICE —

MAYBE WE-WE'LL BE LUCKY AND FARO WON'T DIE...!

NO CHANCE! BIRD BOY PREDICTED IT — HE'S NEVER WRONG!

BIRD BOY IS THE ONE I SEEK — THE JUDGE CHILD! IF I DELAY MUCH LONGER, IT MAY BE TOO LATE!

A STRIP OF SYNTHI-SKIN CONCEALED A MINUTE TRANSMITTER —

HOME IN ON ME, BIKE! STOP FOR NOTHING — THIS IS THE BIG ONE!

DREDD'S BIKE WAS ON COMPUTER CONTROL —

THE GHOST RIDER AGAIN! BLOW HIM AWAY — AAAGH!

OOOOAARROOOOAAAAAARRRR

BLAM-BAM

BLAM-BAM

BLAM-BAM

AAAH!

THIS IS OUR CHANCE!

FREEDOM FOR THE SLAVES!

FTAK! FTAK!

THE STORM THAT HAD BEEN BREWING — ERUPTED!

BAM! BAM!

DEATH TO THE BROTHERHOOD OF TRASH!

BLAM!

TEXAS CITY JUDGES WERE ON THE PIER –

Y'ALL HIT TOWN AT A BUSY TIME, JUDGE DREDD! THE *MUTIE CLEARANCES* HAVE STARTED! WE'RE SHIPPIN' 'EM ALL OUT TO NEW *HOMELANDS* ACROSS LAKE LOUISIANA!

YES. AND NOW I SEEK A *MUTANT* CHILD – WHO WILL ONE DAY BE *CHIEF JUDGE* OF *MEGA-CITY ONE!*

TEXAS CITY WILL *WALK TALL* AGIN WITHOUT THEM UGLIES! Y'ALL OUGHTA KNOW – *YOUR* CITY DID THE SAME THING YEARS AGO!

DREDD EXPLAINED HIS MISSION –

WE CAN'T SPARE YOU ANY HELP, FELLA! *PA ANGEL* AND HIS GANG *BROKE JAIL* YESTERDAY! ANY OF OUR BOYS THAT AIN'T BUSY WITH THE CLEARANCES IS OUT LOOKIN' FOR THEM.

THE ANGELS IS A *BAD* BUNCHA HELL-RAISERS!

I PREFER TO WORK ALONE.

DREDD WAS GIVEN ACCESS TO THE JUSTICE COMPUTER –

THE BOY HAS STRONG *PRE-COG* ABILITY, SO I WANT INFORMATION ON PRE-COGS WHO'VE STARTED OPERATING WITHIN THE PAST TWENTY DAYS... WHAT'S THIS? *BROTHER DEATH...*

...A NEW FAIRGROUND *FORTUNE TELLER* AT *MUTIE-WORLD.* HE'S BEEN UNCANNILY ACCURATE AT PREDICTING HIS CUSTOMERS' DEATHS!

IT'S GOT TO BE *THE MONK!* HE THINKS I'M DEAD – THAT NOBODY'S AFTER THE BOY! HE'D HAVE NO REASON TO ALTER HIS APPEARANCE!

TEXAS CITY BRED BIG MEN WHO LIKED TO LIVE DANGEROUSLY. AT *DANGER PARKS* LIKE *MUTIEWORLD,* A MAN COULD *LEGALLY* RISK HIS LIFE TO PROVE HIMSELF.

SOME CAME OUT *WALKING TALL.* MANY DIDN'T COME OUT AT ALL –

STEP RIGHT UP! *SHAKE HANDS* WITH THE *THING* AND WIN A FORTUNE! ONLY 20 CREDS A TRY!

Y'ALL KIN DO IT, BOBBY JOE!

SHAKE HANDS WITH THE *THING* FROM THE PIT – C10000 IF YOU SURVIVE!

WALK TALL THERE, BOY!

1000 lbs

VERY WELL... I DON'T KNOW YOU, BUT I HAVE MET SOME OF OUR YOUNGER CROP OF JUDGES AND I AM *NOT IMPRESSED* BY WHAT I'VE SEEN...

UNDERSTAND THIS — I DON'T CARRY PASSENGERS. YOU'LL PULL YOUR WEIGHT OR YOU CAN BET YOU'LL HEAR FROM ME!

PHEW! OLD STONEY-FACE IS IN A BAD MOOD TODAY!

FROM WHAT I'VE HEARD, HE'S IN A BAD MOOD *EVERY* DAY!

FROM DREDD'S LOG —

DAY 1 18.00

HEADING OUT OF SOLAR SYSTEM ALONG ROUTE TAKEN BY ANGEL GANG. CREW LOOK GOOD, YOUNG AND KEEN. SLIGHT WORRY ON LOPEZ. DON'T LIKE TO SEE A JUDGE WITH FACIAL HAIR.

20.48:

DELAYING HYPER-DRIVE TO INVESTIGATE SUSPICIOUS VESSEL IN MINERAL FIELDS BEYOND PLUTO...

THIS IS *CAPTAIN JIM FLINT* ON *ECHO BRAVO 4*! OUR LONG-DISTANCE RADIO EQUIPMENT HAS PACKED UP —

PLEASE CONTACT OUR FOLKS AT HOME AND LET 'EM KNOW WE'RE ALL A-OK AND MAKING LOTS OF LOVELY MONEY!

DEEP SPACE DRILLING RIGS CRUSHED THE ASTEROIDS TO EXTRACT VALUABLE TRACE ELEMENTS —

ECHO BRAVO 4 *DISAPPEARED* WITHOUT *TRACE* OVER THREE *YEARS* AGO... THAT'S KINDA LONG FOR A SIMPLE RADIO FAILURE!

ESPECIALLY WHEN THOSE RIGS ONLY CARRY *ONE* YEAR'S SUPPLIES. C'MON, HERSHEY — WE BETTER LOOK INTO THIS!

MEGA TINTO MINING CO EB4

THERE'S NO NEED TO COME ABOARD, JUDGE DREDD! YOU'LL BE IN THE WAY — THIS IS A BUSY RIG, YOU KNOW!

YOU'VE GOT NO CHOICE IN THE MATTER, FLINT!

IN THE ENTRY PORT —

THE *ARTI-GRAV* IS OFF! ACTIVATE YOUR BOOT MAGNETS!

WHAT D'YOU MAKE OF THE NATIVES, JUDGE DREDD?

NOT VERY MUCH, LARTER. KEEP THE ENGINES WARM — WE'RE NOT STAYING!

RRARRR! GRAAAARR!

MOST ODD BEHAVIOUR!

FROM DREDD'S LOG —

NATIVES OF PLANET OMBRA STILL IN PRIMITIVE STATE. NO LIKELIHOOD JUDGE CHILD'S KIDNAPPERS SOUGHT REFUGE THERE. CONTINUING WITH MISSION...

AND THAT IS HOW BUGGO THE WEAK, BECAME BUGGO THE BRAVE —

—AND WHY THE *DREADED FACE OF GOD* IS PAINTED IN HIS CAVE!

NEXT PROG: *MEET PRESIDENT ROCKIN' ROCKY ROCK!*

FROM DREDD'S LOG —

DAY 12 14.30: ENTERING EPSILON SYSTEM. ONLY ONE INHABITABLE PLANET — LESSER LINGO. E.T.A. 17. 47.

LOPEZ PROVING DIFFICULT RE MOUSTACHE. HAVE ORDERED DAILY INSPECTIONS OF THE ENGINE DECK . . .

ENGINE DECK LOOKS FINE, LOPEZ. HERSHEY AND I WILL NEED OUR BIKES ON LESSER LINGO — GIVE THEM BOTH A COMPLETE *OVERHAUL* .

YES, JUDGE DREDD.

WHY DON'T YOU JUST GIVE IN AND SHAVE IT OFF ? YOU'LL CRACK BEFORE OLD STONEY FACE !

BUT IT'S NOT *FAIR*, HERSHEY ! I DUNNO WHAT HE'S GOT AGAINST IT ! THERE'S NOTHING IN *REGS* SAYS A JUDGE CAN'T HAVE A MOUSTACHE !

SOON — THAT'S LESSER LINGO. IT WAS COLONISED BACK IN 2055. ESTIMATED HUMAN POPULATION NOW 250,000 . . .

THERE'S ALSO AN INTELLIGENT *NATIVE* RACE — JUST KNOWN AS "THE ALIENS". THEY'RE EMPLOYED TO DO MOST OF THE *MANUAL* JOBS.

AT THE SPACE PORT —

LESSER LINGO CUSTOMS POINT

MEGA-CITY ONE JUDGES ! CAN I GET THE PORTERS TO HELP YOU —

WE CARRY NO LUGGAGE. JUST PROVIDE US WITH DIRECTIONS TO YOUR POLICE HEADQUARTERS.

PILKINGTON FOR BETTER BIOCHIPS

HERTZ RENT-A-BODY

JOE'S BODY MART: BODIES ON VIEW ALL DAY

WHY DIE ? RENT-A-BODY WITH PICKFORD

RITZ AGENCY BODIES TO THE WEALTHY

BODIES BEAUTIFUL WESCOTT & KRAMER BODY BROKERS

WE MAY FIND THE INHABITANTS A LITTLE STRANGE HERE, HERSHEY. *BIOCHIPPING* IS *LEGAL* ON LESSER LINGO !

BODY BROKERS BODIES BOUGHT & SOLD (ALL GRADES)

BEST BODIES

BANNED IN MEGA-CITY ONE, THE BIOCHIP PROVIDED A MEANS FOR THE WEALTHY TO PROLONG THEIR LIVES . . .

WHEN DEATH APPROACHED, A CUSTOMER COULD VISIT ONE OF THE MANY BODY BROKING AGENCIES ON THE PLANET —

I'LL HAVE THAT ONE! I'VE ALWAYS WANTED TO BE A BLONDE!

MARILYN IS ONE OF OUR TOP BODIES, MRS SUTCH. SHE IS AVAILABLE FOR FOUR HOURS A DAY AT TWO HUNDRED CREDITS PER HOUR. THE USUAL PENALTY CLAUSES IF HER BODY IS DAMAGED WHILE IN USE.

AT THE MOMENT OF DEATH, THE CUSTOMER'S PERSONALITY WAS PROGRAMMED ONTO THE TINY BIOCHIP — A LIVING MACHINE —

THE BIOCHIP WAS THEN IMPLANTED INTO A PREPARED SOCKET IN THE HIRED BODY, PROGRAMMED TO TAKE OVER CONTROL FOR A SET TIME EACH DAY (MAXIMUM OF 10 HOURS) . . .

WITH THE BIOCHIP, DEATH COULD BE DELAYED FOREVER —

DON'T YOU RECOGNISE ME, FINLAY? IT'S YOUR MOTHER!

— OR AT THE LEAST UNTIL THE MONEY RAN OUT!

AT POLICE HQ, DREDD EXPLAINED THEIR MISSION TO POLICE CHIEF WINSTON NYE —

SO THIS ANGEL GANG STOLE THIS JUDGE KID! CAN YOU BEAT THAT? CAN'T REMEMBER ANY SUSPICIOUS ARRIVALS ON-PLANET, BUT YOU'RE WELCOME TO CHECK OUR RECORDS!

POLICE CHIEF

DEAR ME, THIRTEEN O'CLOCK. I'LL HAVE TO LEAVE YOU TO IT, JUDGE. I HAVE A *BODY RENTAL* COMING UP.

IT'S THE LATE MRS MURDSTON, SHE HIRES ME BECAUSE SHE LIKES MAKING ARRESTS. BIT UNUSUAL BEING A DAME, BUT FOR 7B.50 AN HOUR I'M NOT COMPLAINING! WHO CAN LIVE ON A POLICEMAN'S PAY THESE DAYS?

NIGHT, MRS MURDSTON.

NIGHT, BOYS. GIVE MY REGARDS TO THE CHIEF WHEN YOU SEE HIM.

DREDD'S SEARCH DREW A BLANK—

WE COULD LOOK FOR YEARS AND NEVER FIND WHERE THEY'VE TAKEN THE BOY! WE'VE GOT TO FIND SOME WAY OF *NARROWING* THE SEARCH!

OUTSIDE—

I'VE BEEN ASKED TO ESCORT YOU TO *VICE-PRESIDENT KOLBEG'S* OFFICE, SIR!

SOON—

THAT'S VICE-PRESIDENT KOLBEC?

YES AND NO... ALL THE HUMAN LEADERS DIED YEARS AGO. THAT'S THE VICE-PRESIDENT'S *BIOCHIP* IN IVOR GOULGONOV'S BODY.

THE VICE-PRESIDENT HAS TO KEEP IT IN GOOD CONDITION AS PART OF THE AGREEMENT.

GLAD YOU COULD COME ALONG, JUDGE DREDD. WE GOT OURSELVES A LITTLE PROBLEM HERE. *PRESIDENT CARLYLE HAS BEEN KIDNAPPED!*

THE PRESIDENT RENTED THE BODY OF ROCKIN' ROCKY ROCK, THE POPSTAR. LAST WEEK ROCKY WAS SNATCHED BY *WILD ALIENS!* WE FOUND ROCKY THREE HOURS LATER. HIS BIOCHIP HAD BEEN *REMOVED!*

I KEPT TELLING HIM — GET A BIG STRONG BODY! BUT NO! HE WANTED TO BE THE MAN OF THE PEOPLE.

THERE YOU HAVE IT, JUDGE. OUR OWN POLICE ARE TOO UNRELIABLE AND THE ALIEN CONSTABULARY ARE AFRAID TO GO INTO WILD ALIEN COUNTRY.

I'M ASKING *YOU* TO RESCUE THE PRESIDENTIAL BIOCHIP!

OOOFFA!

I'VE HEARD ABOUT YOUR MISSION. HELP US AND IN RETURN I CAN OFFER YOU *ORACLE-SPICE!*

ORACLE-SPICE! YOU HAVE IT?

I KNOW WHERE IT CAN BE FOUND.

THE SPICE IS SAID TO GIVE IMPORTANT KNOWLEDGE TO THOSE WHO TAKE IT. WITH IT WE COULD FIND THE BOY.

I ALWAYS THOUGHT IT WAS A *MYTH* — BUT MY LIE-DETECTOR SAYS HE'S TELLING THE TRUTH!

BAM BAM

VERY WELL.

I AGREE.

GREAT! NUMBER 49 HERE WILL GUIDE YOU. HE'S THE ONLY ONE OF THE BLIGHTERS I COULD GET TO VOLUNTEER.

POLICE 49

SOON —

THIS IS THE ALIEN QUARTER, WHERE ALL US CIVILISED ALIENS LIVE.

CIVILISED?

OUT THERE — THAT'S *WILD* ALIEN COUNTRY!

HAS DREDD HAD HIS BIOCHIPS? FIND OUT IN JUDGE CHILD 2!

61

SO YOU'RE THE AMBASSADORS FROM ORRTEN. EH ? LISTEN, KIDS, I DUNNO ZILCH ABOUT THIS PRESIDENT HOOHA ! WHADDYA SAY WE GET TOGETHER ON A LITTLE DUET, HUH ? IF YOU DON'T KNOW THE WORDS, JUST GRUNT ALONG —

BEFORE DEATH, PRESIDENT CARLYLE'S ENTIRE PERSONALITY HAD BEEN PROGRAMMED ONTO THE TINY *BIOCHIP*. WHEN IT WAS *IMPLANTED* IN ROCKY ROCK'S *SKULL*, THE PRESIDENT ONCE AGAIN TOOK CONTROL OF THE BODY —

I'M AFRAID ROCKY CAUSED THREE *INTERPLANETARY INCIDENTS* WHILE HE WAS COVERING FOR YOU, MR PRESIDENT !

NOT ONE OF OUR TAME CONSTABLES ! A *WILD* ONE — ONE WITH *WINGS* !

DAYS LATER, THE BIOCHIP WAS IMPLANTED IN THE SKULL OF A WILD ALIEN. FOR TEN HOURS EACH DAY, HE WOULD BE *PRESIDENT CARLYLE* !

THAT SO, EH ? WELL, THERE'S NOTHING FOR IT BUT TO RENT A NEW BODY. SEND FOR AN ALIEN —

WHEN DID YOU DECIDE ON YOUR ALIEN BODY, UH, MR PRESIDENT ?

I GOT BITTEN BY THE FLYING BUG WHEN THE ALIENS SNATCHED ME, NOTHING LIKE IT ! YOU DON'T KNOW WHAT YOU'RE MISSING !

OF COURSE, THIS WILL MEAN *EQUAL RIGHTS* FOR *ALIENS* ! AS PRESIDENT, I CAN'T TOLERATE *DISCRIMINATION AGAINST MY OWN RACE* !

BY THIS TIME, DREDD WAS MANY LIGHT YEARS AWAY —

DAY 17 01.00 HEADING FOR THE HADEAN SYSTEM, A LITTLE-KNOWN GROUP OF PLANETS DEEP IN THE GALAXY. ACCORDING TO VICE-PRESIDENT KOLJAC, WE WILL FIND THE ORACLE SPICE THERE. WE *MUST* FIND IT — OR I AM CONVINCED WE WILL NEVER FIND THE JUDGE CHILD.

NEXT PROG:
THE HUNGRY PLANET !

THE JUDGE CHILD

THE JUDGE CHILD
PART 12

BATTLEGROUND

DREDD'S SEARCH FOR THE JUDGE CHILD
CONTINUES ACROSS THE GALAXY...

FROM DREDD'S LOG—

DAY 40   12.00

APPROACHING PLANET AGROS IN THE MYSTERIOUS
HADEAN SYSTEM. LITTLE INFORMATION EXISTS
ABOUT AGROS — SAVE THAT THERE ARE TWELVE
INTELLIGENT RACES — ALL OF THEM AGGRESSIVE.

I THINK I'M BEING *KISSED!* HOW DO WE TELL THESE CREEPS TO STOP?

TINY MICRO-PROCESSORS WERE ATTACHED TO THE JUDGES' THROATS, CAPABLE OF TRANSLATING HUMAN SPEECH INTO ANY ALIEN TONGUE.

A HELMET PROCESSOR SIMULTANEOUSLY TRANSLATED ALIEN TO HUMAN.

AS DOK SPOKE, THE TRANSLATOR BEGAN TO PICK UP THE LANGUAGE — ...A FEW DETAILS FOR THE FOLKS AT HOME, JOHN!

MY NAME IS JUDGE DREDD! I WANT NO PART IN THIS WAR OF YOURS! I HAVE QUESTIONS TO ASK — *TAKE ME TO YOUR LEADERS!*

SORRY, JOHN! RULES SAY NOBODY LEAVES THE FIELD OF PLAY TILL THE BATTLE'S OVER!

AND WHAT ABOUT YOU, JOHN? ANY REACTION TO BEING DECLARED A *NATURAL HAZARD?* SURPRISED?

NOT AT ALL. I EXPECTED TO RUN INTO LOONIES ON THIS MISSION.

OUR *TRANSLATORS* SHOULD BE WORKING SOON!

THERE YOU HAVE IT, FOLKS! STRAIGHT FROM THE BRZOG'S MOUTH! NOW WE'RE GOING OVER TO *DIK* BECAUSE I UNDERSTAND THE *SECOND PHASE WEAPONS* ARE COMING ON!

YES INDEED, DOK! THIS COULD BE THE TURNING POINT IN THE WARGAME! THE *GALLIPARDAN NATIONS* HAVE DRAWN *BATTLE TANKS* FROM *EPTURA* — NO MATCH FOR THE *PAZAZZ WAR WHEELS* THE *LURGANS* WILL BE USING!

THERE'S GOING TO BE SOME *GREAT SLAUGHTER* IN THIS *SECOND HALF!*

THE JUDGE CHILD

90

NEXT PROG: *AFTER THE WAR —*
THE HORROR !

THE JUDGE CHILD

THE JUDGE CHILD

DAYS EARLIER, IN ANOTHER PART OF THE GALAXY —

DAY 51: 20.04
MISSION TO FIND ORACLE-SPICE SUCCESSFULLY COMPLETED. NOW WE WILL SEE IF IT POSSESSES THE POWER THEY CLAIM — IF IT CAN LEAD US TO THE JUDGE CHILD...

IN MED BAY —

ONE LIFE for EVERY DROP of ORACLE SPICE. A DEVIL'S BREW! IF THE JUDGE CHILD WASN'T SO IMPORTANT TO US, I'D DESTROY IT HERE AND NOW!

RATHER YOU THAN ME, JUDGE DREDD! NO TELLING WHAT THAT FILTHY STUFF WILL DO TO YOU!

IT WON'T DO ANYTHING TO ME, LOPEZ. YOU'RE GOING TO TAKE IT.

WHY ME? IT'S BECAUSE OF MY MOUSTACHE, ISN'T IT?

YOUR PERSONALITY PROFILE SHOWS YOU TO BE THE MOST UNSTABLE MEMBER OF THIS CREW —

THE MOST RECEPTIVE TO INFORMATION FROM THE ORACLE SPICE. NOW KINDLY GET ON WITH IT!

LOPEZ WAS STRAPPED DOWN —

WE'LL START WITH ONE DROP. NO TELLING WHAT THE PROPER DOSE IS. EVEN THIS MUCH COULD KILL YOU!

YOU KNOW HOW TO SAY ALL THE RIGHT THINGS, HERSHEY!

THE EFFECT WAS ALMOST INSTANT —

ANYTHING TO REPORT, LOPEZ...?

THINGS WARPING — TWISTING... YOUR FACES — STRETCHED LIKE...LIKE RUBBER...

AND THEN NIGHTMARE VISIONS CROWDED IN ON LOPEZ —

BEWARE THE ORACLE! BEWARE!

AIEEEE!

JUDGE LOPEZ, WE NOW COMMIT YOUR BODY TO THE DEPTHS OF SPACE!

LOPEZ!

FROM DREDD'S LOG –

DAY 73 : 12.00
APPROACHING PLANET AB.
COMPUTER GIVES THEIR
LANGUAGE AS **ALLSPEAK**.*
SO NO COMMUNICATION
PROBLEMS.
LOPEZ STILL IN COMA. CONDITION
GIVING GRAVE CAUSE FOR CONCERN.

* ALLSPEAK – UNIQUE ALIEN
FORM OF SPEECH WHICH IS
UNDERSTOOD IN ANY LANGUAGE.

HE'S GROWING WEAKER,
SIR. WE'VE TRIED
EVERYTHING TO BRING
HIM ROUND.

YOU STICK BY HIM, HERSHEY.
IF HE SAYS ANYTHING ELSE,
I WANT TO KNOW ABOUT IT.

IF HE **EVER** SAYS
ANYTHING !

AB – WHAT LAWS APPLY
IN THIS WORLD I DO NOT
KNOW. IT IS A LAW
UNTO ITSELF,
UNEXPLAINABLE –
ALIEN . . .

THEY'VE GOT AN UNUSUAL
LINE IN ARCHITECTURE,
ANYWAY !

DREDD WAS TAKEN TO POLICE HEADQUARTERS –

YES, ONE OF YOUR RACE ENTERED THE
PLANET ILLEGALLY SOME WEEKS AGO.
PROSSER IS HIS NAME.

NAMES CAN BE CHANGED.
THEY MEAN NOTHING.
WHERE IS HE ?

ALL **ILLEGAL ALIENS** ARE
KEPT IN THE **FOOT
BUILDING** UNTIL SUITABLE
ARRANGEMENTS CAN BE
MADE TO **DEPORT** THEM.
PROSSER IS THERE . . .

WHAT'S WRONG, PROSSER ?
COME ON, PLAY GAME !

GAMES ! HOW CAN I
PLAY GAMES WHEN I'M
DISAPPEARING INTO
THIN AIR ?

UHH! IT GET REAL WORSE! I GLAD JIGSAW DISEASE NOT CATCHING!

MY EYE JUST WENT! TH-THERE'S **GOT** TO BE A CURE! THEY'RE LYING TO ME! I'M AN ALIEN, SEE — THEY DON'T CARE WHETHER I LIVE OR DIE! IT'LL SAVE THE COST OF DEPORTATION IF I JUST **FADE AWAY!**

I'M GONNA **MAKE 'EM** GIVE ME THE CURE!

IN THE FOOT BUILDING SICK BAY —

WHERE ARE THE PILLS? THERE'S GOTTA BE **PILLS!**

I **KNEW** IT! YOU LIED TO ME! THERE **IS** A CURE!

NO, DON'T TAKE THEM —

TRY AND STOP ME!

YOU DOCTORS ARE ALL THE SAME, HUMAN OR ALIEN. TREATMENT FOR THE RICH AND THE POOR CAN JUST DIE!

I'M NOT GOING TO DIE! I'M FINDING A WAY OFF THIS CRAZY PLANET BEFORE ANYTHING ELSE HAPPENS TO ME!

WHEN DREDD ARRIVED —

JIGSAW DISEASE IS A WASTING AWAY OF THE BODY IN STRANGELY REGULAR PATTERNS. WE DON'T KNOW WHAT CAUSES IT — IT JUST HAPPENS.

SKIP THE CHAT! THIS PROSSER TOOK THE PILLS AND RAN OFF...?

IF YOU WANT HIM YOU'LL HAVE TO HURRY. YOU SEE, I **WASN'T** LYING. THERE IS NO CURE FOR THE DISEASE.

THE PILLS HE TOOK WERE A MERCY DRUG. THEY **SPEED UP** THE RATE OF THE DISEASE. THE WAY HE WAS TAKING THEM, I RECKON HE'LL BE **GONE WITHIN THE HOUR!**

NEXT PROG: **PROSSER, THE PUZZLE... AND PA ANGEL!**

115

THE **PILLS** HE TOOK ARE A **MERCY DRUG** TO **SPEED UP** THE **JIGSAW DISEASE**. THE WAY HE WAS TAKING THEM, HE'LL BE **GONE WITHIN THE HOUR** !

PILLS ! COME BACK ! YOU'RE MY ONLY CHANCE !

PILLS WILL STOP THIS NIGHTMARE — THEY'VE **GOT** TO !

SUDDENLY —

PLEASE ! NOT MY **FINGERTIPS** ! NOT **NOW** !

AAAAH!

THERE HE IS !

OH, NO ! AN ESCALATOR TO NOWHERE ! CURSE THIS CRAZY PLANET !

DROKK THIS PLANET ! THE HARD PART IS GOING TO BE GETTING TO HIM !

WHEN DREDD FINALLY REACHED THE JIGSAW MAN HIS BODY WAS IN THE FINAL STAGES OF DISINTEGRATION —

DROKK ! HARDLY ANY FEATURES LEFT TO IDENTIFY... BUT I'D SWEAR HE'S **NOT** ONE OF THE JUDGE CHILD'S KIDNAPPERS...!

"I ASKED HIM..."

WILL PROSSER COLLECT HIS MONEY? HA HA HA HA! FUNNY QUESTION!

WHY? WHAT'S WRONG?

DISEASE TAKES YOU! NO HANDS TO HOLD YOUR MONEY – NO EYES TO SEE! HA HA! ALL THE KING'S HORSES AND ALL THE KING'S MEN, WILL NEVER PUT HUMPTY TOGETHER AGAIN!

THEY SAY THE KID'S NEVER WRONG!

YEEHAA! THAT SOUNDS FUN, PA! KIN I HAVE PROSSER IN MY CABIN SO'S I KIN WATCH HIM DIE, HUH, PA?

DON'T BE A DANGED FOOL, JUNIOR! IF IT'S A DISEASE, WE COULD ALL CATCH IT!

THE COMPUTERS'LL HAVE TO HANDLE THE SHIP... PROSSER'S GOTTA GO!

...SO THEY SET ME ADRIFT IN AN ESCAPE POD. I FOUND MY WAY TO THIS CRAZY PLANET... AND HERE I AM...

AND "ALL THE KING'S HORSES" WON'T PUT YOU TOGETHER AGAIN. YES... LOPEZ SAID SOMETHING SIMILAR UNDER THE ORACLE SPICE...

AS THE STORY UNFOLDED, PROSSER HAD BEEN SLOWLY FADING AWAY –

WHERE AM I GOING? OH, HELP, WHAT'S TO BECOME OF ME?

I CAN'T EXPLAIN THE UNEXPLAINABLE... YOU'VE HELPED MY CITY FIND THE JUDGE CHILD, PROSSER, TAKE THAT THOUGHT WITH YOU...WHEREVER YOU'RE GOING...

BUT DON'T YOU SEE? I CAUGHT THE DISEASE HERE! IF THE KID HADN'T TOLD THEM, THEY'D NEVER HAVE SET ME ADRIFT! I'D STILL BE ALIVE!

THE BOY KILLED ME – AS SURELY AS IF HE'D STUCK A KNIFE IN MY HEART! HE SENT ME TO MY DEATH – AND HE LAUGHED ABOUT IT!

YOUR PRECIOUS JUDGE CHILD IS EVIL!

EVIL!

POP!

THE **FINAL PIECE** OF THE **JIGSAW MAN**... WAS **GONE**!

THERE IS SOME TRUTH IN WHAT HE SAID... **FARO** DIED IN THE SAME WAY*...ONLY BECAUSE THE BOY **PREDICTED** IT...

LATER, BACK ABOARD JUSTICE 1 —

THE BOY USED THE SAME WORDS AS LOPEZ — "ALL THE KING'S HORSES WON'T PUT HUMPTY TOGETHER AGAIN..."

THEY WON'T PUT LOPEZ TOGETHER AGAIN EITHER. HE DIED THIS MORNING.

LOPEZ HAD TAKEN **ORACLE SPICE** IN ORDER TO FIND A CLUE TO THE JUDGE CHILD'S WHEREABOUTS —

ONE DROP OF ORACLE SPICE — AND IT WAS TOO MUCH!

WHAT I WANT TO KNOW IS, **WHY HIM**? YOU'RE IN COMMAND HERE — WHY DIDN'T **YOU** TAKE THE FILTHY STUFF?

LOPEZ WAS THE MOST RECEPTIVE TO ORACLE SPICE — THE ONLY CHOICE. HE KNEW THE RISKS AND HE ACCEPTED THEM. TRY TO FOLLOW HIS EXAMPLE, HERSHEY!

DAY 74: 13.00
THIS MORNING WE COMMITTED LOPEZ'S BODY TO SPACE. EVERY JUDGE MUST BE PREPARED TO GIVE HIS LIFE FOR THE CITY. WHEN HIS MOMENT CAME, LOPEZ WAS NOT FOUND WANTING. HE WILL BE REMEMBERED.

TEARS AGAIN FROM HERSHEY. THIS IS UNDERSTANDABLE — HER FIRST EXPERIENCE OF THE DEATH OF A COMRADE. SHE'S A GOOD JUDGE, SHE'LL LEARN...

WHAT WORRIES ME IS THE **JUDGE CHILD**... HE'S MORE THAN JUST A PRE-COG — HE CAN **TWIST** THE **FUTURE**, **MANIPULATE** IT — AND NOT ALWAYS FOR **GOOD**...

THIS CHILD MY CITY IS DEPENDING ON, IS TOUCHED BY A. . . A **STREAK OF EVIL**!

* SEE PROG 159.

121

THE JUDGE CHILD

XANADU — A BARREN, VOLCANIC ROCK ON THE FAR EDGE OF THE JOHANNSEN CLUSTER. DECLARED AN "OPEN PLANET" 2078. AS SUCH, HAS BECOME THE HAUNT OF FUGITIVES FROM ALL OVER THE GALAXY. NO DOUBT WE WILL MEET SOME FAMILIAR FACES. THEY MUST BE IGNORED. OUR ONLY BUSINESS HERE IS TO FIND THE ANGEL GANG — AND THE JUDGE CHILD...

JUSTICE ONE'S INSTRUMENTS LOCATED THE ANGEL GANG'S HIJACKED SPACE CRAFT — CRASHED IN A LARGE SETTLEMENT —

THAT'S WHAT HAPPENS WHEN YOU KILL YOUR PILOT!

SCAVENGERS ALREADY AT WORK! OKAY, LET'S CUT THIS SHORT! HERSHEY — GET THE XANADU CURRENCY...

DREDD ADDRESSED THE CROWD —

MY NAME IS DREDD! SOME OF YOU MAY KNOW ME! SOME OF YOU MAY EVEN BE HIDING FROM ME! IF SO, THIS IS YOUR LUCKY DAY! I DON'T WANT YOU!

I'M HERE FOR ONE THING ONLY — THE CREW OF THAT STARSHIP!

GO HOME, LAW JOCKEY! NOBODY ON XANADU TELLS THE LAW NOTHING!

MAYBE THIS WILL CHANGE YOUR MINDS!

MONEY!

IF THERE'S ONE THING I'VE LEARNED, THERE'S NO HONOUR AMONG CRIMINAL SCUM LIKE THEM. SOMEONE WILL TALK, SOONER OR LATER...

AND PROBABLY SOONER!

IT'S RAINING MONEY!

THERE'S TWO MORE SACKS WHERE THAT CAME FROM — FOR THE MAN — OR THING — THAT CAN LEAD ME TO THE ANGEL GANG!

NEXT PROG: THROUGH THE EYES OF THE BLIND!

141

ANOTHER THREE CUSTOMERS IN BACK, UNDERTAKER!

THANKEE, JUDGE!

SINCE DREDD ARRIVED ON XANADU, THE UNDERTAKER HAD DONE BRISK BUSINESS —

THIS PLANET NEEDS A FEW JUDGES... BUT I'M CONCERNED ONLY WITH THE JUDGE CHILD'S KIDNAPPERS — THE ANGEL GANG!

SOONER OR LATER, SOMEONE IS GOING TO TRY TO GET THE *REWARD* I'M OFFERING THE *EASY WAY* — BY *TALKING*...

MEANWHILE, IN THE TOWN OF DRYBONE —

ORDER! ORDER! THE **COURT** OF **DRYBONE** IS NOW IN SESSION — **JUDGE JUNIOR ANGEL PRESIDIN'!**

THIS TOWN IS CHARGED WITH BEIN' **DULL** AN' **BORIN'**, AN' NOT HAVIN' ENOUGH **KILLIN'!**

MISTER PROSECUTOR **LINK**, WHAT IS THE FIRST CASE?

THIS HERE BEANBAG IS GUILTY OF **BREACH OF THE PEACE** — TO WIT: **BLEEDIN' IN A PUBLIC PLACE!**

IT'S NOT TRUE! I HAVEN'T!

YOU HAVE NOW, SEE?

THE PROSECUTION RESTS!

CASE PROVED! GUILTY! HANG HIM! NEXT!

DRYBONE'S LUCK HAD **DRIED UP** THE DAY THE ANGELS CAME INTO TOWN —

HEY, JUNIOR, BETTER NOT KILL ANY MORE — ELSE THERE WON'T BE **NOBODY LEFT** FOR US TO **BULLY!**

DON'T BE DUMB, LINK! WHEN THEY'RE ALL DEAD, WE JES' UP AN' MOVE TO ANOTHER TOWN!

147

153

VERY WELL! BRING HIM TO ME AND WE WILL **SEE**...

BUT BE WARNED! I DO NOT GIVE YOU SAFE PASSAGE. MANY OF MY SUBJECTS ARE FUGITIVES FROM HUMAN OPPRESSION...

THE JOURNEY TO MY CASTLE IS LIKELY TO PROVE **FATAL**...

PA HEADED FOR THE DISTANT VOLCANIC HILLS —

HUMANS!

LOOKEE, PA! **HAIRY ROBOTS!**

NOW HOW IN TARNATION KIN ROBOTS GROW HAIR?

BLAM·BLAM·BLAM!

IT'S **HUMAN** HAIR, YOU FOOL! THEY **IMPLANT** IT IN THEIR **METAL**. IT'S THEIR FORM OF TAKING **SCALPS!**

WHEE-DOGGIE! THIS HERE **GRUNWALD** SURE 'PEARS TO BE A **REAL FUN PLACE!**

MEANWHILE, HOURS BACK ALONG THE TRAIL, OLD JOE BLIND HAD BURIED HIS FAITHFUL HORSE —

GUESS THAT MEAN MACHINE CRACKED HIS SKULL WHEN HE BOPPED HIM. ONLY **HATE** KEPT HIM GOING THIS LONG —

159

WE'LL MAKE BETTER TIME NOW ! YOU ALL RIGHT, OLD TIMER ?

RECKON I AIN'T GONNA DIE TILL THE LAST TWO ANGELS FALL ! KEEP RIDIN', JUDGE DREDD ! THAT WAY !

IT WAS EVENING WHEN DREDD REACHED THE BOUNDARY OF GRUNWALD — THAT THERE'S **ROBOT COUNTRY**. THE **GRUNWALDER** USES ROBOT INSECTS AS WATCHDOGS. THEY'VE GOT RADIOS IN 'EM — CATCH ONE AND YOU CAN SPEAK TO THE GRUNWALDER.

I SEE THEM —

YOU ARE NOW ENTERING, GRU

MOMENTS LATER —

GRUNWALDER! I AM **DREDD – JUDGE** OF **MEGA-CITY ONE** ! I COME FOR THE **BOY** WITH THE **EAGLE MARK** !

THE WAY HE SPEAKS, GRUNWALDER ! ALMOST LIKE A ROBOT HIMSELF !

AND BESIDES, ATTACKING HIM MIGHT **WELL** PROVE EXPENSIVE IN ROBOT LIVES !

I WILL BROOK **NO INTERFERENCE** WITH MY MISSION. ANY PERSON OR ROBOT WHO GETS IN MY WAY WILL BE **EXECUTED** UNDER SECTION 34b OF THE **SECURITY OF THE CITY** ACT.

YOU HAVE BEEN FORMALLY **WARNED**.

YES ! THERE IS **STEEL** BENEATH THAT FLESH. GIVE THE ORDER – HE IS NOT TO BE ATTACKED. I AM MOST INTERESTED TO SEE WHAT HAPPENS WHEN HE MEETS THE OTHER HUMANS . . .

THE **ANGELS** CAMPED IN THE VOLCANIC FOOTHILLS. TOWARDS DAWN —

HEY, PA ! **BALDY'S** GONE INTO ONE A' THEM THAR **TRANCE** THINGS ! I TOLD HIM TO **QUIT** THAT OR I'D **KILL HIM** !

YOU WON'T KILL ME, IMBECILE ! YOU KNOW WHY ? BECAUSE **YOU'RE** GOING TO DIE ! JUST LIKE **LINK** AND THE **MEAN MACHINE** DIED !